FRIGHTS

To all the people who have helped me face my fears! I now have a torch and I'm not afraid to use it! Thankyou! Lisa xoxo

One Tentacle Publishing
PO Box 3058
Uki, New South Wales, 2484
Australia

www.onetentaclepublishing.com

First published in Australia in 2019

A catalogue record for this book is available from the National Library of Australia

ISBN 978 0 6480068 7 9

Editor: Matt Ottley
Cover font *Jokoowi*

FRIGHTS

LISA TIFFEN

One night Heath’s mum said...

"Goodnight! Sleep tight!" and turned off the light.

That was when some Frights came and jumped on Heath's tummy.

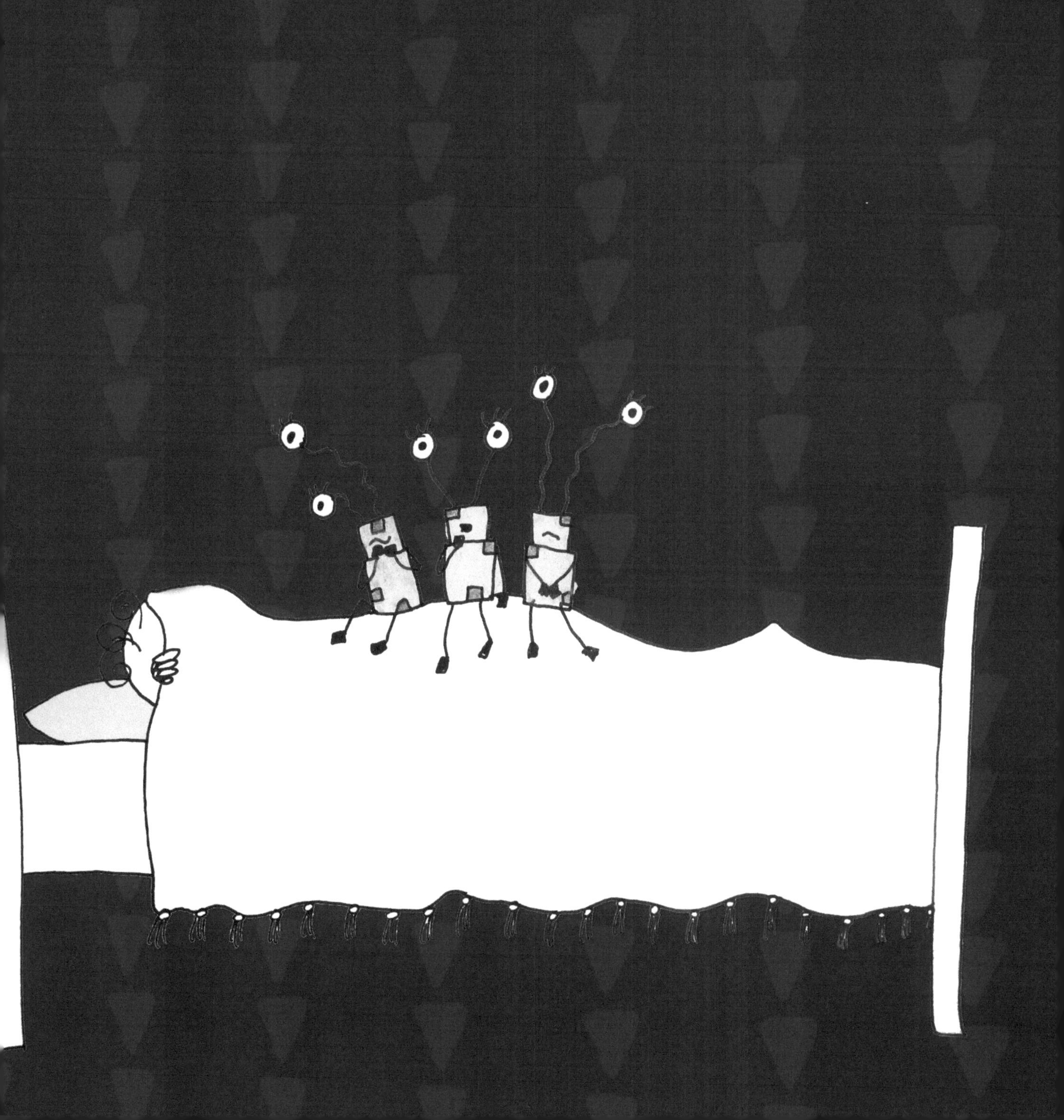

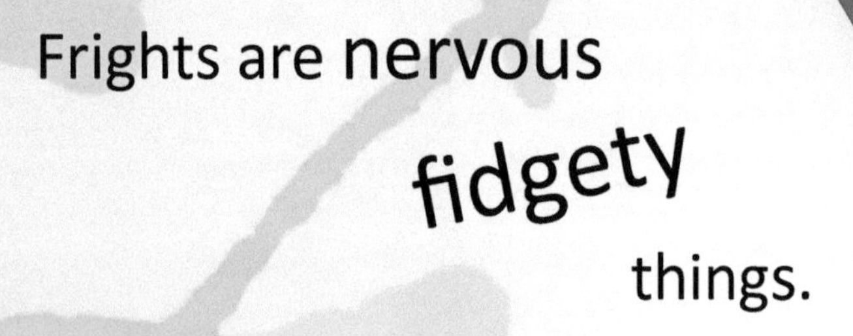

Frights are nervous

fidgety

things.

They chew on their fingers

and hide

behind their hands.

Frights have
anxious
darting
eyes.

Frights smell sickly sweet
like sugary food and
stinky cheese.

Their pongy perfume
goes right up your nostrils
until you grow dizzy and
feel you can't breathe.

Their smell makes your stomach swirl and swish.

Frights are scared of new and different things.
NO, THIS HAIRSTYLE IS WAY TOO CRAZY FOR ME!
NO WAY! TOO DANGEROUS!!

Their favourite saying is

"I can't!"

They hide themselves away...

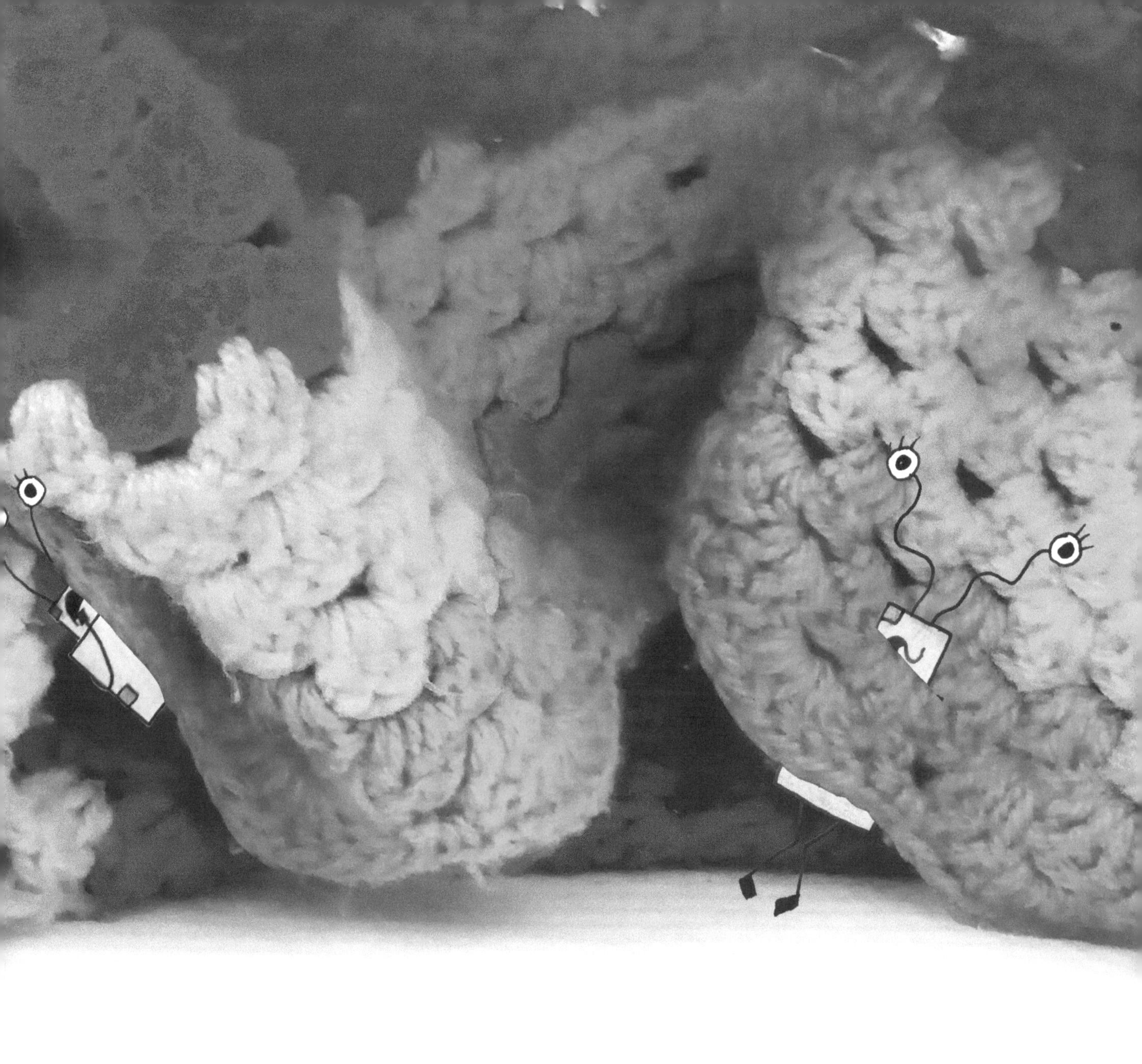

and peek out from time to time.

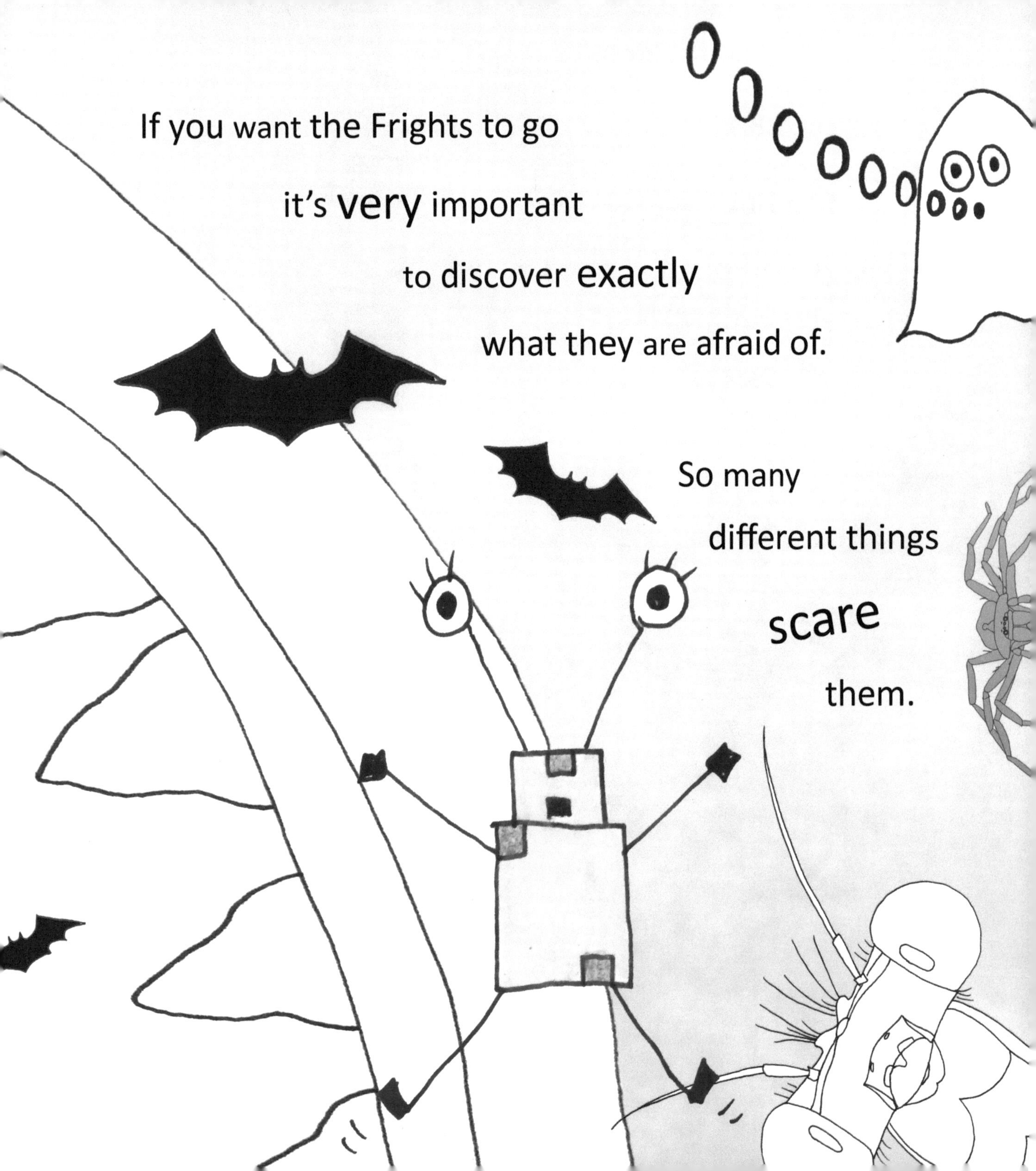
If you want the Frights to go
it's very important
to discover exactly
what they are afraid of.
So many
different things
scare
them.

Frights can be
hard
to get rid of.

Sometimes
you need a friend's
helping hand.

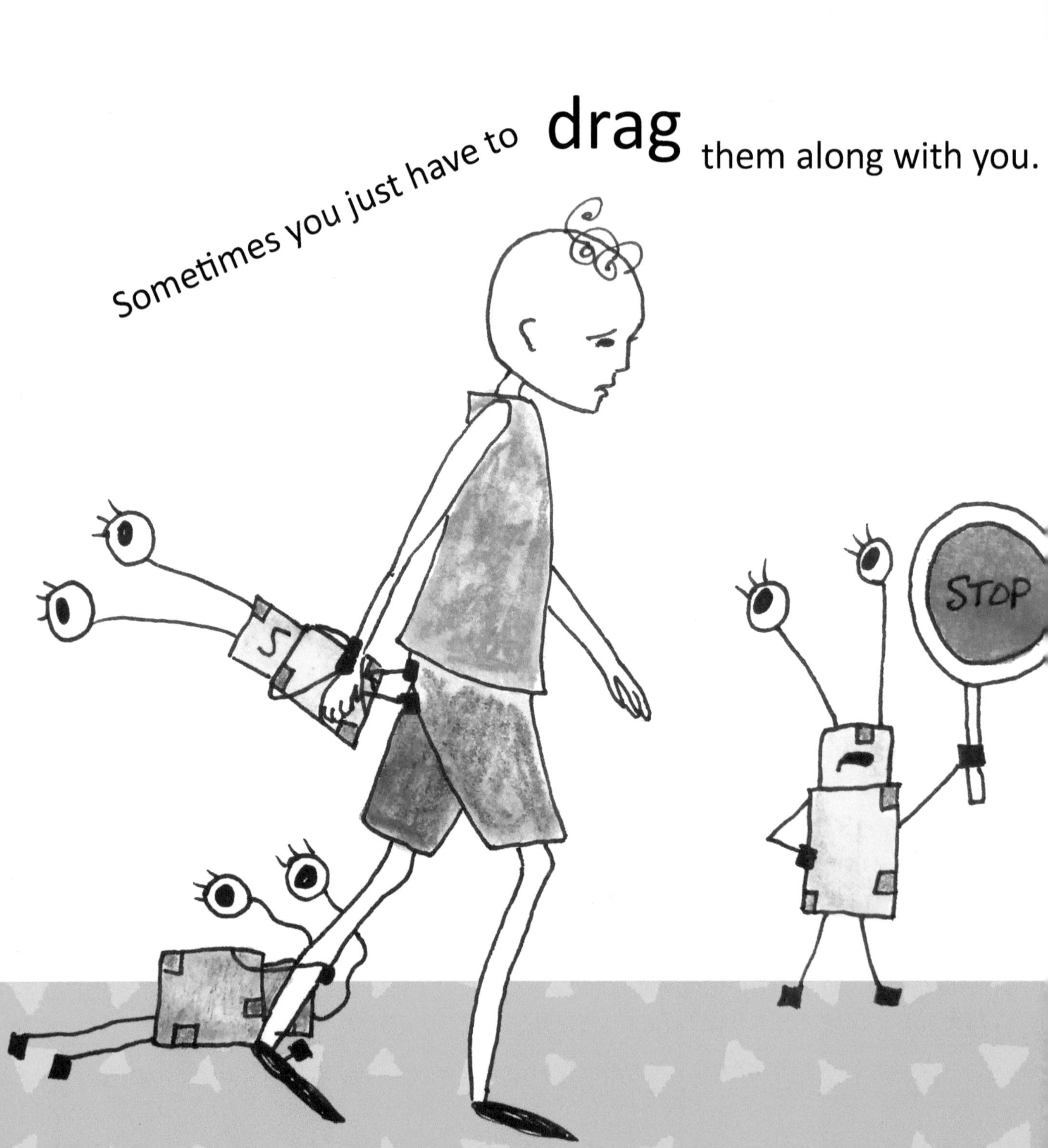
Sometimes you just have to drag them along with you.
S
STOP

This takes a **lot** of determination!

But the **best** way to free yourself of the Frights is...

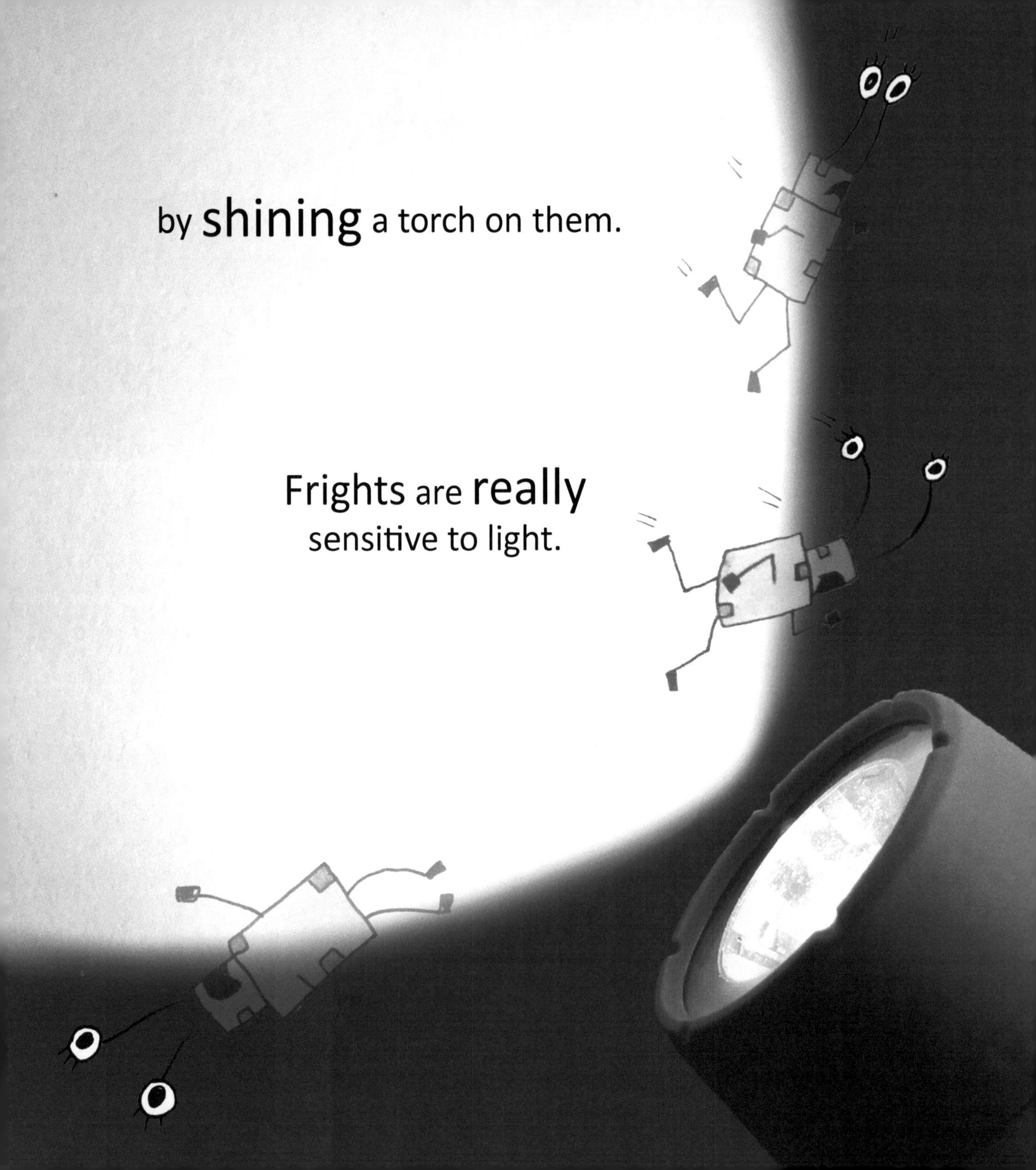

by **shining** a torch on them.

Frights are **really** sensitive to light.

Lisa Tiffen lives in northern New South Wales, Australia, with her husband and four children, who provide her with a lot of laughs and much inspiration.

Frights is her fourth picture book.
Stay tuned for more!

www.lisatiffen.com

CPSIA information can be obtained
at www.ICGtesting.com
Printed in the USA
BVHW021721300519
549718BV00008B/59/P